INTRODUCTION

---◆---

Butterflies throng in rainforests and kaleidoscope by rivers. Their origami forms flutter through meadows and thrill on garden blooms. Eighteen thousand species range across each continent bar Antarctica and inhabit almost every island in between. Butterflies are everywhere – and they are ours to enjoy, to revere. This book celebrates their existence, their wonder, their diversity.

It is butterflies' *differences* that enthral. Their variation inspires awe – their seemingly infinite takes on what it *means* to be a butterfly. Some glide effortlessly on wings of lace; others blaze in fiery flight. There are exuberantly gregarious species and unrepentantly solitary ones. Many inhabit the forest canopy; others live at ankle height. They range in size from your fingernail to your forearm.

Each species follows a survival strategy – but few are precisely the same. Some butterflies rely on camouflage to conceal their forms from sharp-

eyed predators. Others have evolved patterns to simulate animals that eat those predators. Some deploy splashes of traffic-light red or amber to warn carnivores that they ingested poisons as caterpillars. Others free-ride, mimicking genuinely toxic butterflies to dupe birds into believing they are also worth avoiding.

There are surprises too. Butterflies that emerge only after dusk, generate loud noises or consume animal faeces rather than floral nectar. Microscopic wing structures that refract light into shimmering colours. Con-artist butterflies that parasitize unwitting ants. Cryptic new species – hiding in plain sight, undetected by scientists. Species that shed novel light on evolutionary processes.

But, above all, butterflies enchant by serving as a metaphor for our own life journey. With their metamorphosis from insignificant caterpillar to winged wonder, butterflies persuade us that anything is possible. We too can renew, regenerate and transform. This book expresses our gratitude to these most special creatures.

COMMON
BANDED PEACOCK
Papilio crino

- - - ◆ - - -

WINGSPAN: *100–116mm (4–4½in)*
RANGE: *Asia, Australasia*

Keep your eyes directed upward in moist or dry evergreen forests of southern or eastern India – or, indeed Sri Lanka, Nepal or Bhutan – and you may spot a large black-and-green butterfly hurtling through the sub-canopy. A type of swallowtail, the common banded peacock spends most of its life high in the trees, where it imbibes flower nectar. If you are lucky, it may drop to the understorey, fluttering urgently as it feeds on bright-red blooms of the genus *Ixora*. Occasionally this butterfly alights on the ground, where its predominantly dusky

underwings enable it to blend with the typically dark soils on which its favoured forests flourish.

The most remarkable feature of the common banded peacock is its upperwing coloration. A vibrant cyan-green band cuts a swathe through broad black wings dusted with tiny green dots. The coloured areas are iridescent, shimmering as they catch the light. Experts in the field of nanophotonics have recently investigated how this butterfly produces such shifting coloration. Using an electron microscope, they have determined that the wing scales have a variably concave surface, comprising minute ridges and furrows, and that the green shades we perceive result from the way in which yellow and blue light bounces around these tiny structures.

Females can sometimes be spotted laying eggs on the leaves of the Ceylon satinwood *Chloroxylon swietenia*, a mid-sized deciduous tree with slightly corky bark and creamy-coloured florets. Its pinnate leaves provide all the nourishment needed by common banded peacock caterpillars. Populations of this tree have declined through over-exploitation: the golden colour of its wood is appreciated in the furniture industry. Although the current status of common banded peacock remains true to its name (i.e. common), its future is clearly contingent on that of the Ceylon satinwood.

TROPICAL BUCKEYE

Junonia evarete

— — — ◆ — — —

WINGSPAN: *45–57mm (1¾–2¼in)*
RANGE: *Americas*

Few butterflies have caused as much confusion over their identity as the tropical buckeye and its almost-identical sister species, the mangrove buckeye (*Junonia genoveva*). Both were described as new to science based on individuals collected in Suriname (in northern South America) during the late seventeenth century. Unfortunately, these individual butterflies ("type specimens", in biologist-speak) were lost – and all that remained were Dutch naturalist Pieter Cramer's hand-coloured engravings (reproduced here).

It was the interpretation of these illustrations that caused such problems. Research in 2008 revealed that, for decades, many butterfly experts had

interchanged the two species, thinking that mangrove buckeye was tropical, and vice versa. Given that the most reliable way to distinguish them involves checking minute differences in the colour of the underside of the antennae, such an error is understandable.

Careful study of the species' ecology has led to a more useful way to distinguish the two, whose ranges overlap. Tropical buckeye inhabits weedy disturbed habitats where the caterpillar's food-plant – blue porterweed (*Stachytarpheta jamaicensis*) – flourishes. In contrast, the larval larder of mangrove buckeye is black mangrove (*Avicennia germinans*), so it tends to be found along muddy shores washed by the sea.

This fast-flying butterfly frequently perches on the ground with its wings opened, revealing four eyespots (*ocelli*). In butterflies, these are thought to have one of two purposes. Firstly, they intimidate predators such as insectivorous birds into fleeing; peacock (*Inachis io*) exemplifies this strategy. Alternatively, the *ocelli* deflect bird attacks to less vital parts of the body. Buckeyes are judged to exemplify the latter rationale.

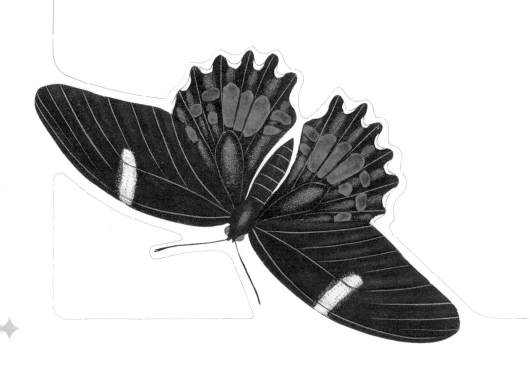

RUBY-SPOTTED
SWALLOWTAIL

Papilio (Heraclides) anchisiades

— — — ◆ — — —

WINGSPAN: *70–100mm (2¾–4in)*
RANGE: *Americas*

Butterflies flutter by. Fun to say, but also true for many species, including swallowtails in the 200-strong grouping known as Papilionini. These glorious insects flicker their wings rapidly while feeding, as if too nervous to relax completely.

Unlike most members of its "tribe", the ruby-spotted swallowtail lacks the protrusion on the hindwing that gives swallowtails their name. A common insect, it has an enormous range, stretching 8,000km (5,000 miles) from southern Texas to northern Argentina. It is easily recognized

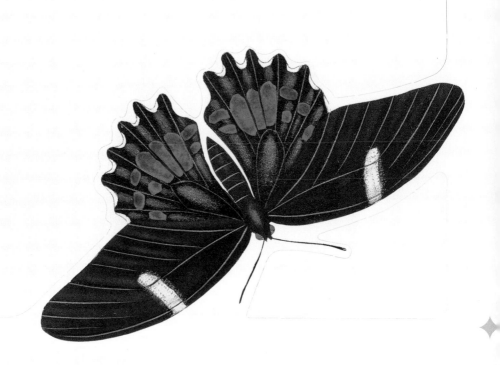

by its long black wings adorned with ruby and white patches.

But such familiarity conceals a degree of uncertainty. Taxonomists – biologists who decide how species fit into the wider scheme of life – are in dispute as to how closely related the various swallowtail species are. Many lepidopterists consider that, evolutionarily, they are all much of a muchness – and house the lot in a single genus, *Papilio*. Others reckon that those swallowtails inhabiting the New World tropics ("Neotropics"), such as the ruby-spotted, should be separated out as the genus *Heraclides*.

This alternative scientific name for the genus illustrates the respect that taxonomists often display for Greek mythology. A Heraclides was a member of the clan Heracleidae, who were descended from Heracles, the son of Zeus. Heracles is the god of strength, so his association with swallowtails reflects their size and perceived might. Greek or Roman figures often feature in a butterfly's scientific name, which otherwise often honours a real person, some aspect of the species's appearance or where it lives. In this instance, *anchisiades* relates to Anchises, who was considered as beautiful as the gods – not a bad scientific name by which to be known.

ULYSSES
SWALLOWTAIL

Papilio ulysses

- - - ◆ - - -

WINGSPAN: *105–140mm (4–5½in)*
RANGE: *Australasia*

In the gloom of the New Guinea rainforest, a mysterious neon light is flashing Morse code. Or so it seems. The reality is no less bizarre. The sporadic glimpses of electric blue are the upperwings of the Ulysses swallowtail, an enormous butterfly.

Also known as the blue emperor, the Ulysses swallowtail occupies tropical forests throughout much of New Guinea, Maluku, the Bismarcks and the Solomons, and sneaks into Australia in eastern Queensland. It is roughly the Australasian equivalent of the morphos (*Morpho*) of

Central and South America. Like those Neotropical butterflies, the Ulysses swallowtail might easily be overlooked at rest, when the dark-brown coloration of its closed wings merges with the sylvan murk.

When it takes to the wing, however, everything changes. Moreover, once one Ulysses swallowtail is airborne, the likelihood is that another will follow. Males may sit still for hours at a time, waiting for the flash of emergency-service blue that potentially announces the arrival of a female. So keen are males to mate that they may zip through the forest to investigate *anything* bright blue, whether or not it is their female quarry. Butterfly collectors have exploited this by waving a metallic-blue object, to lure their prized specimen into a net.

The Ulysses swallowtail has become a neat tourist attraction in northeast Queensland. Such service has been facilitated by this butterfly's flexible approach to living: although ostensibly a denizen of the rainforest, it has adapted to life in the suburbs, enticed by the planting of pink-flowered doughwood (*Mellicope elleryana*), its food-plant. Indeed, the Ulysses swallowtail has become so widely known that it has been featured on Australian postage stamps – not just once but three times since the 1980s.

MALABAR TREE NYMPH

Idea malabarica

◆

WINGSPAN: *120–154mm (4¾–6in)*
RANGE: *Asia*

High in the air, what appears to be a white handkerchief is floating in leisurely fashion across a rainforest clearing. It turns out to be a butterfly, and a mighty one at that. The Malabar tree nymph is related to the monarch (*Danaus plexippus*), a famous New World butterfly. But the tree nymph is considerably larger – some individuals are half as big again as a monarch – and arguably more beautiful. It is one of the heftiest butterflies on the Indian subcontinent, as big as a typical man's hand.

On rounded, translucent wings of glassy white, this apparent paper kite glides between the crowns of tall trees, barely bothering to flap.

Its progress is unabashedly slow – comfortably lethargic rather than stately. Such a manner of flight ought to make the Malabar tree nymph a straightforward target for aerial predators. Yet birds know to leave it alone. In common with other members of the butterfly grouping known as Danaini, its striking wing pattern sends a clear message: "I am toxic. I taste bad and will make you ill. Leave me be."

Each morning, Malabar tree nymphs ascend to the forest canopy to feed on the flowers of *Syzygium* (the genus of cloves, a widely used spice). As the day weaves towards a close, small groups of up to half a dozen butterflies wend their unhurried way downwards, parachuting and circling before alighting on vegetation around 5m (16½ft) above ground.

BLUE MORMON

Papilio polymnestor

---◆---

WINGSPAN: *120–140mm (4¾–5½in)*
RANGE: *Asia*

At no more than knee height above the lawn of a garden in suburban Mumbai, India, two gargantuan butterflies are dancing. Even in this ultra-urban metropolis inhabited by a barely conceivable 18 million people, there is natural beauty. Moreover, the performers – blue Mormons, India's second-largest butterfly – have struck a chord with the people of Mumbai and its state of Maharashtra.

In June 2015, in the middle of the blue Mormon's main flight season, government officials broke new ground by declaring this stunning electric-blue and glossy-black insect India's first state butterfly. For a country where conservation awareness appears focused on charismatic "megafauna" (big

animals) such as tigers, affording official status to otherwise unappreciated insects appears a bold and arguably enlightened move.

And what a butterfly to choose. Although a denizen of humid rainforests by preference, particularly in the Western Ghats, the blue Mormon has been enticed into the concrete jungle by a profusion of nectar-rich plants, particularly jasmines and citrus trees, in carefully attended gardens. In doing so, it has made itself accessible to the masses.

The "dance" is a courtship display, led by the female. She hovers rapidly above the ground, the male imitating her every move barely one wingspan behind her. She appears to be testing his stamina and dexterity – how long can he go on for? And how perfectly can he follow her every move? – presumably as an indication of the robustness of his genes, and thus his suitability as a mate.

As the butterflies fly in synchrony, so the inky droplets embedded in the bright-blue swathe of their wings appear to flicker, mesmerizing the observer. A worthy state butterfly indeed.

TAWNY RAJAH

Charaxes bernardus

◆

WINGSPAN: *70–90mm (2¾–3½in)*
RANGE: *Asia*

Butterflies that occur at a low density – their populations sparsely distributed over a large area rather than concentrated in a colony – face a significant problem. If they are to breed, they need to find one another. The predicament is magnified for those butterflies that inhabit dense forests: how can encounters take place if the insects cannot see one another?

The tawny rajah and other members of the genus *Charaxes* are among a group of butterflies that face this problem – but have evolved a strategy to deal with it. Known as "hilltopping", this approach involves both sexes commuting daily to the highest point in the vicinity, which

is usually either a hilltop (hence the strategy's name) or a particularly tall tree (as is often the case in the rainforest habitat favoured by the tawny rajah). Having found one another, courtship, and potentially copulation, can proceed.

Other well-known "hilltoppers" include the purple emperor (*Apatura iris*). Although the emperor and rajah are unrelated, they share two other noteworthy characteristics: both are very fast fliers, powering through the canopy or across clearings, and both also profess a superficially unseemly taste for animal dung. Locating and waiting near animal faeces in an Indian forest may not be top of your bucket list, but it is one of the best ways to see a tawny rajah. Males descend to the ground, using their proboscis to probe the excrement and extract minerals.

In the absence of such suitable waste, rajahs routinely "mud-puddle". This involves imbibing mineral salts dissolved in damp ground. The behaviour is only known among male rajahs, and seems to occur particularly following copulation. The hypothesis is that the flaming-orange males need to replenish salts lost during courtship and mating.

MOUNTAIN APOLLO

Parnassius apollo

------◆------

WINGSPAN: *62–95mm (2½–3¾in)*
RANGE: *Europe, Asia*

Two thousand metres (6,600ft) above sea level, in the soaring rocky landscape of Spain's Picos de Europa, it is summer. What little turf grows here is stippled with coloured flowers. Nevertheless, it feels hard to imagine butterflies at this altitude.

Perhaps the mountain Apollo is more deity than butterfly. It certainly makes an authoritative entrance, coasting emphatically on ivory-coloured tissue-paper wings that rustle audibly in the crisp stillness of the montane air. Then it lands, the better to allow your admiration.

At close range, mountain Apollo wings are almost translucent. Whereas 6,000 scales cover every square centimetre of most butterflies' wings, the

Apollo has far fewer. Such a sparse covering explains the wings' glassy appearance. This is not to imply that they are devoid of colour: black spots and bars decorate the forewing, and each hindwing flames with fiery eyespots, each rimmed black and encasing a tiny snowy dot.

These concentric circles warn predators that the Apollo tastes bitter – a legacy of its days as a caterpillar, munching on white stonecrop (*Sedum album*), which imparts an unpleasant chemical, a cyanoglucoside, now concentrated in the Apollo's wings. One montane bird, the water pipit (*Anthus spinoletta*), has worked out that removing the butterfly's wings eliminates the problem – enabling it to consume the nutritious, toxin-free body.

The stakes are high for montane butterflies. A cold snap mid-summer, and insects may die before procreating. This may be why the male mountain Apollo seeks to guarantee his paternity by sealing the female's genital opening with a gelatinous plug (termed "sphragis"), which prevents the female from mating with any other male. The challenge is accented by climate change, and recent atmospheric warming has been blamed for the dramatic decline of the mountain Apollo across much of Europe.

SICKLE-WINGED MORPHO

Morpho rhetenor

— — — ◆ — — —

WINGSPAN: *140–170mm (5½–6¾in)*
RANGE: *South America*

An electric flash of royal blue. Gone. A metallic glint of neon. Gone. An eye-searing flare of cobalt amid Amazonian obscurity, the iridescent sickle-winged morpho alternately dazzles and confuses as it flops erratically through the rainforest understorey. With more extensively blue wings than any other of the forty-odd members of the genus *Morpho*, there may be no more beautiful butterfly in the whole of South America.

The morpho is the New World tropics' most iconic insect, garnishing many a tourist brochure. It may even be the most widely recognized

butterfly in the world, its formidable size and irrepressible coloration setting the standard for lepidopteran aspirations. But it has captivated people to its own detriment. Morpho wings have been plucked by indigenous Amazonian tribes to embellish ceremonial masks, while Western collectors have long prized framed assemblages of morpho specimens.

The morpho's blue iridescence derives from the interplay of light on minute yet complicated structures in wing scales. The ever-changing sheen is thought to enable males to communicate with one another. Meanwhile, the butterfly's slow, bouncy flight is a consequence of relying on a small body to pump disproportionately huge wings.

The combination of iridescence and flight manner serves as a defence mechanism called "flash coloration". The glittering blue has a considerable downside, attracting the unwanted attention of avian predators such as flycatchers. The bird gives chase, only to become bemused as the butterfly disappears each time it closes its wings, revealing their discreet brown underside. Then the butterfly suddenly switches from sedate perambulation to an evasive swoop. Accelerating onto a branch, it snaps shut its wings and freezes. The bird is now completely bewildered. Its search image – a large bright-blue insect – has vanished into thin air. The sickle-winged morpho is done with dazzling; now it seeks to confuse.

GREAT MORMON

Papilio memnon

- - - ◆ - - -

WINGSPAN: *120–150mm (4¾–6in)*
RANGE: *Asia*

Butterflies typically live for just a few short weeks – some for mere days. Their lives are a headlong rush to breed before natural causes overcome them or they succumb to predation. Chances of producing a lineage are improved the longer the butterflies can stay alive. Accordingly, many species of butterfly have evolved impressive strategies to elude the clutches of hungry carnivores.

Disguise is one; think of the leaf-like comma (*Polygonia c-album*). Decoys are another, attracting the predator's attention to a non-critical part of the butterfly – hence the tails on a Madagascar giant swallowtail (*Pharmacophagus antenor*). A third option is "diematic defence", whereby butterflies such as

the peacock (*Inachis io*) scare predators by resembling a larger carnivore such as an owl.

The great Mormon, a common swallowtail that occurs over much of Asia, deploys a fourth strategy, termed "Batesian mimicry". This honours Henry Bates, who, in 1862, presented the case that palatable butterflies occasionally produce mutations with visual characteristics that resemble those of noxious species. Bates argued that such similarity would make the mutations less likely to be eaten, so their characteristics would be inherited by their offspring. Over time, bluffing would become a successful strategy.

In the great Mormon, Batesian mimicry is taken to an extreme. The female has twenty-odd forms, a phenomenon known as "polymorphism". Collectively, these exhibit variation in tails (presence or absence), forewing pattern, hindwing pattern and the colours of the wing base and abdomen. Many of the female forms copy toxic species, particularly roses in the genus *Atrophaneura*. Extensive study of great Mormon forms has revealed that the mimicry is controlled by a "supergene" complex, the effectiveness of which builds up over time to allow accurate imitation.

SPANISH FESTOON

Zerynthia rumina

❖

WINGSPAN: *44–48mm (c.1¾in)*
RANGE: *Europe, Africa*

What looks like a miniature swallowtail (*Papilio machaon*) glides – directly but not noticeably strongly – low over the ground. As the Spanish festoon pauses to drink from a minuscule pink floret of wild thyme on the Iberian *garrigue*, it allows a better look. Although much smaller than any of the European swallowtails, the festoon exhibits a similar pattern of wan-yellow upperwings overlain with jagged lines, bars and braces. Even experts do not claim to know whether mimicry is involved, but the purpose of this arrangement is certainly similar to the larger species: to break up the form of the butterfly, thereby confusing predators.

The Spanish festoon is an early-season butterfly, flying for a few short weeks in April and May. A single brood is commonplace, although there are suggestions that it manages to breed twice in southeast Spain.

This butterfly's common name is more exclusive than is justified by its actual distribution: Spain may claim this particular festoon, but it actually occurs throughout Iberia, in southern France and across the Mediterranean into North Africa. Wherever Spanish festoons live, their preferred terrain encompasses dry scrub such as *maquis* or *garrigue*. Such habitat demands provide an ecological separation from the very similar southern festoon (*Zerynthia polyxena*), which occupies damper habitats over a wide swathe of Europe and western Asia.

However, nature is rarely entirely cut-and-dried. After a recent extensive fire in southeast France, the regenerating vegetation was dry, enabling the Spanish festoon to spread into the range of the southern festoon, so much so that a mixed pair was observed for the first time ever. Whether this was a one-off event or the start of evolutionary warfare is as yet unclear.

CLOUDED YELLOW

Colias croceus

------◆------

WINGSPAN: *46–52mm (1¾–2¼in)*
RANGE: *Europe, North Africa, Middle East, Asia*

Peering southwards across the English Channel during the Second World War, British military lookouts were initially mystified, then increasingly concerned, before being astonished when they finally grasped what was coming their way. At distance, all that the observers could decipher was a huge golden ball. As the glowing, floating sphere approached, they feared it was a cloud of poison gas. Yet this was no cloud, but rather clouded yellows – an immense swarm of one of the world's great migrant butterflies.

Essentially a species of North Africa and the Mediterranean, clouded yellows flood northwards through Europe in spring. Every decade or so,

the migration assumes the magnitude of an invasion. Butterfly experts delight in such "*Edusa* years", a term that refers to the butterfly's former genus name.

This migratory prowess results in two notable achievements. First, it arguably renders clouded yellow the most widespread butterfly in Europe. Second, it enables this master colonist to populate new areas. Most remarkably, the clouded yellow is one of just six species of butterfly to have established itself on the Azores, a North Atlantic archipelago some 1,450km (900 miles) from the nearest population in continental Spain.

Observing a clouded yellow at close range is no mean feat, for these are skittish butterflies, apt to fly hundreds of metres in a burst should they feel threatened. If a careful approach proves successful, however, scrutinize the butterfly's underwing to see the impressive veins that transport blood to the muscles that power its migration.

As its name suggests, clouded yellow is a vigorously saffron-coloured butterfly. Five females in every hundred, however, are whitish or pale grey. This form (known as *helice*) is thought to reflect particularly dry conditions during development of the chrysalis.

RED ADMIRAL

Vanessa atalanta

WINGSPAN: *64–78mm (2½–3in)*
RANGE: *Europe, Africa*

Being common throughout its extensive range, frequently admired in urban gardens and easily recognized thanks to blazing bands across its wings, the red admiral is among the world's most familiar butterflies. Yet widespread conversancy with this insect has only recently been matched with accurate comprehension. For centuries, the red admiral hugged tightly the secrets of an unexpectedly complex lifestyle. It has taken twenty-first-century technology, complemented by concerted citizen science, to unravel the mystery.

In appearance, the red admiral is a butterfly of two halves. The black, white and scarlet coloration of its upperwing serves both to attract mates

and shock predators. But when perched with its wings folded, this creature blends seamlessly with its surroundings. The underside of the rear wing is densely mottled and delicately swirled with browns and greys, providing camouflage adequate for the butterfly to feed or roost unmolested.

It is not only visually that the red admiral is somewhat cryptic. Although lepidopterists have long known that it migrates – an uncommon practice among most butterflies – much of their collective understanding has proved erroneous.

Until recently, it was incorrectly believed that red admirals squeezed two broods into the north European summer before migrating southwards to hibernate as adults. The reality is that the second crop of adults respond to autumn's falling temperatures by fleeing towards the Mediterranean without mating. They migrate either within a metre of the ground or – a secret revealed by radar studies – at high altitude, having first soared upwards on thermals of rising air.

Upon arrival in the Mediterranean, the butterflies have surprised scientists further, by breeding rather than hibernating. It is the offspring of this southern generation that mature over the winter before winging northwards as adults in the spring.

ORANGE-TIP

Anthocharis cardamines

- - - ◆ - - -

WINGSPAN: *40-52mm (1½-2in)*
RANGE: *Europe, Middle East, Asia*

Patrolling a grassy woodland glade in search of receptive females, the male orange-tip is often taken to signal the arrival of spring. This compact butterfly – a member of the Pieridae, the family comprising whites and yellows – takes its name from the fluorescent tangerine stripe on the male's forewing. The colourful splash warns predatory birds that the butterfly tastes unpleasant – a legacy of the bitter mustard oils accumulated from food-plants during the caterpillar stage.

The female has no such need to advertise her distastefulness. She eludes predators by a combination of behaviour and camouflage. Unlike the incessantly airborne male, the female flies as little as

necessary, and relies upon her marbled moss-green underwing to conceal her presence. So different are the sexes that they were given different names in the mid-eighteenth century: Prince of Orange (for the male) and wood lady or lady of the woods (female).

One component of the female is orange, however: her eggs. When searching for a suitable crucifer on which to lay her ovum, the female will ignore any flower head that is already adorned by an egg. Even if she fails to spot the egg, she should be able to "smell" it, because females deposit a pheromone while laying eggs. The combination of colour and scent deters the new arrival, which is just as well, since cannibalism accounts for one-tenth of the deaths of young orange-tip caterpillars: the first-born eats any conspecifics it encounters.

Climate change is altering the orange-tip's life cycle. In the UK, a 1 per cent temperature rise in the late twentieth century correlated with an advance in the flight season of 17 days. The orange-tip is also spreading north here, regaining territory from which it disappeared during the nineteenth century.

COMMON BIRDWING

Troides helena

— – – ◆ – – —

WINGSPAN: *130–180mm (5–7in)*
RANGE: *Asia*

The name gives it away. The common birdwing is a huge, majestic beast. The female's wingspan matches that of birds such as house sparrow (*Passer domesticus*). It is a looker too, with shimmering velvet wings gleaming with golden-yellow streaks, spots and splodges that power a body of fire decorated with crimson, lemon and coal.

Such a striking appearance conveys an unequivocal message: do not eat me, for I am toxic. This communication is honest; the common birdwing is genuinely noxious, not a harmless mimic claiming to be unpalatable. The adult birdwing's bad taste derives from a vine called Indian birthwort (*Aristolochia tagala*), nibbled during its early life as a caterpillar.

There are 20 further species of birdwing in Asia and Australasia, all rainforest dwellers and all resembling the common birdwing, with wings pitting black against gleaming yellow. The common birdwing has the widest distribution, occurring from India to Taiwan. Other species are markedly restricted, some constrained to a single island, particularly in Indonesia. Such a limited range puts them at considerable threat of extinction from deforestation.

Male common birdwings are often seen circling through the forest canopy in the morning. They are searching for females, which tend to sit quietly amid dense, verdant foliage. Should a male strike gold, discovering a female, he quivers a courtship dance several metres above her. If she is impressed, the male is permitted to descend and mate.

The common birdwing is so highly prized by collectors that international trade in it is now regulated through the intergovernmental agreement known as CITES (Convention on International Trade in Endangered Species). Such market demand makes the birdwing's situation particularly parlous. Its existence is already predicated on the continued survival of its sole larval food-plant, Indian birthwort. As deforestation destroys this vine, so the common birdwing finds it harder to breed.

LARGE BLUE

Maculinea arion

--- ◆ ---

WINGSPAN: *38–52mm (1½–2in)*
RANGE: *Europe, Asia*

The large blue and its four sister species in Europe (all housed in the genus *Maculinea*) have quite the strangest lifestyle of any of the world's 18,000 species of butterfly. Many blue butterflies in the family Lycaenidae (which forms more than one-third of the world total) have developed a remarkable, mutually beneficial relationship with ants. But not the "large blue quintet", whose strategy is unabashedly murderous.

The traditional relationship between blues and ants is for the latter to protect caterpillars in exchange for drinking nutritious secretions produced by the larvae. The large blue and its brethren knock this for six. The con-artist caterpillars exude an odour that deceives workers

of *Myrmica* red ants into believing that they are an ant grub which has somehow escaped from the nest. The workers diligently "return" the errant youngster to its "home". Whereupon the caterpillar expresses its gratitude by slowly consuming the host's true grubs. By the time the caterpillar is ready to pupate, it has eaten more than a thousand grubs, and increased its weight one-hundred-fold. The relationship between the species is very far from mutually beneficial.

And yet there is a twist. Although there are scores of *Myrmica* red ant species across Europe, the "con" only works in the large blue's favour with one particular species. The caterpillar is five times more likely to emerge into a butterfly when housed in the nest of *Myrmica sabuleti*, which is the particular species whose odour the caterpillar mimics. Any other red ant species and the caterpillar is likely to die in the nest. This is because the "nurse ants" that care for grubs are less easily fooled than the workers. They determine that the "grub" does not smell precisely like their species – and set about feeding the imposter to their own kind.

PURPLE EMPEROR

Apatura iris

◆

WINGSPAN: *70–92mm (2¾–3⅔in)*
RANGE: *Europe, Asia*

High above ground, at the summit of a mighty oak tree, two triangular black beauties do battle. The male purple emperors twist and thrust into one another. Each pugilist strives to exert dominance as this grants ownership of the "master" tree to which generations of female emperors have been drawn. The inferior male concedes defeat, melting in retreat into the woodland canopy. The victor swoops and wheels above the dense leafy layer, gliding effortlessly on muscular flicks of massive wings. And then astonishes by exploding downwards to alight on the ground, where it shocks further by feasting on dog faeces.

The purple emperor is an exquisite morass of contradictions. Although regally garbed in glittering purple and coruscating velvet, it loves slurping minerals from the smelliest of food, particularly after mating. It is disdainful of human company, spending most of its life out of our sight on lofty thrones, yet it is peculiarly undisturbed by our presence, deigning to grant an audience at mealtimes.

Throughout its expansive range, the purple emperor emerges in late June, and flies well into August. Males and females congregate around high points in their woodland home, where the males fight for access to mating rights. Neither sex visits flowers, surviving instead on aphid honeydew that coats many deciduous trees in mid-summer. Males alone also descend to ground level to access dung, rotting matter and other pungent yet mineral-rich "foods". An irresistible combination of beauty, rarity and elusiveness means that Europe's second-largest butterfly has long captivated human imagination. Butterfly literature from centuries past glitters with hyperbole about "this noble Fly" and "Royal Game". The carefully chosen scientific name reflects such reverence: Iris was the Greek goddess of the rainbow, and the winged messenger of the Olympian gods.

PEACOCK BUTTERFLY

Inachis io

- - - ◆ - - -

WINGSPAN: *50–55mm (c.2in)*
RANGE: *Europe, Asia*

Few butterflies are simultaneously glamorous and canny – and none masters the combination quite like the peacock. Resting with its wings closed on a tree trunk, it can be near impossible to discern. With its raggedy shape and gently vermiculated browns and greys on the underwing, the butterfly is a doppelgänger for a discarded desiccated leaf. Concealment is its first line of defence against being eaten.

Should a peacock feel threatened, it flashes open its upperwings. Whereas a human may admire the butterfly's glorious coloration (the glamour), a predator such as a mouse or bird is startled by the wings' pattern (the canny). If the butterfly is perched head down, two iridescent

blue circles on its hindwings, each ringed with lemon yellow, jolt the would-be predator into fearing that it has come face to face with an owl. Suddenly, the predator risks becoming prey – and scarpers.

Should you doubt me, try turning this book upside down. See how the blue spots appear to be huge eyes? And how the dark rear (now upper) edge of the butterfly's hindwings appears to lead to an owl's ear tuft? And how the peacock's hairy body passes for the owl's hooked beak? And if I now tell you that the butterfly is able to conjure up an irate hissing sound by rubbing its hind- and forewings together? The shock may be sufficient to send you running, too…

Which would be a shame, because the peacock is a simply stunning creature. It is also very familiar, being a common visitor to gardens, including in towns. This ubiquity is encouraged by its particular taste for nectar produced by buddleia (*Buddleja davidii*) bushes, which commonly flank railway lines and other brownfield sites in northern Europe.

COMMON GREEN
BIRDWING

Ornithoptera priamus

---◆---

WINGSPAN: *180–220mm (7–8¾in)*
RANGE: *Australasia*

A regal butterfly deserves the name of a king. The scientific moniker of common green birdwing (*priamus*) is a nod to the king of Troy during the Trojan War. Only male birdwings of the genus *Ornithoptera* are brightly coloured: iridescent – almost fluorescent – green in the case of most forms of common green birdwing. Although larger (as is normal among butterflies), females exhibit none of the male's showiness. Indeed, being dingy brown better equips them for stealthily laying eggs without attracting the attention of predators.

Once they have emerged from the chrysalis, male common green birdwings have but one objective: to produce descendants. Accordingly, they spend mornings patrolling through their tropical rainforest home. Flying low over the ground, they search the undergrowth for virgin females that have broken free of their pupa that very morning. Each male claims possession of an area of the forest; any intruding male (or even bird) is likely to be chased away. Should the male spot a female, he hovers above her, releasing pheromones designed to entice her into copulating.

Exactly how many species of *Ornithoptera* birdwings exist is a conundrum that has vexed lepidopterists for more than two centuries. Current thinking suggests that there are 13 – although achieving consensus on what constitutes a "species" rather than a "subspecies" or even a "form" is a never-ending challenge. Since the mid-eighteenth century, an astonishing 99 subspecies of common green birdwing have been described – many occurring only on tiny Pacific islands. Some have been elevated to full species: one example is Australia's Cairns birdwing (*Ornithoptera euphorion*). Other purported subspecies have been dismissed as mere variants – causing some cautious authorities to propose that just six subspecies are valid.

PLAIN TIGER

Danaus chrysippus

---◆---

WINGSPAN: *70–80mm (2¾–3¼in)*
RANGE: *Africa, Europe, Asia, Australasia*

If it were legitimate to ascribe emotions to a butterfly, one might expect the plain tiger to be jealous of its close relative the monarch (*Danaus plexippus*). The latter is better known, its migratory feats renowned and its beauty revered. Yet the plain tiger is no less amazing.

This butterfly is able to power across the Sahara Desert and Atlantic Ocean in its quest to colonize new lands. It has spread across the entire African continent and through most of Asia, and established itself on many South Pacific islands en route to Australia. It can exist in barren, rocky land – although it is not averse to slurping nectar from urban gardens. Despite its underwhelming name, the plain tiger is as stunning a

creature as the monarch. Being similarly flaming orange, black and white has earned it an alternative moniker of African monarch. Moreover, this particular king has been long revered. Depicted on an Egyptian tomb three and a half thousand years ago, it was the first-ever butterfly recorded in history.

One secret of the plain tiger's success has been repeatedly copied by other butterflies. It is toxic to predators, harbouring chemicals ingested from plants, which cause heart or liver problems. The tiger's coloration serves as a warning. Numerous butterflies, including the African mocker swallowtail (*Papilio dardanus*), have piggybacked on its message, evolving a colour pattern simulating that of the plain tiger.

Examine the upper hindwing of the male plain tiger illustrated here. Do you see an oval-shaped black spot close to the dark rear border? This is the "sex-brand" (or, formally, the androcomial organs). The males – only – of many species of butterfly possess these. During courtship, the male draws the female's antennae over this part of the wing, which releases pheromones designed to get her "in the mood".

TWO-TAILED PASHA

Charaxes jasius

--- --- ◆ --- ---

WINGSPAN: *65–90mm (2½–3½in)*
RANGE: *Africa, Europe*

D on't go looking for a two-tailed pasha, it is said. Let it come to you.
Better still, invite it for a drink. It sounds odd, but a good place to
encounter this prodigious, dramatically patterned butterfly is at a bar
along the Mediterranean coast, in a dry, wooded area harbouring the
pasha's larval food-plant, the strawberry tree (*Arbutus unedo*).

This butterfly definitely has a thirst on. In the natural world, the
pasha's taste for alcohol is sated by fermenting sap or rotting fruit. But
it has learnt that human habitation provides sources of liquid alcohol,
and it is not uncommon for the butterfly to swoop onto a table and
insert its surprisingly red proboscis into a slick of spilt beer. Lap up too

much, however, and the intoxicated insect can have problems returning to the air…

More than 90 per cent of the almost 200 species of the genus *Charaxes* inhabit tropical Africa. The two-tailed pasha is the only species that scrapes north into Mediterranean Europe. Here it crams two broods into the year, one in spring and the other in late summer. Like other *Charaxes*, it is strongly territorial. Males assume position atop a tall tree, surveying their domain. Should a pasha spot an intruder, it exhibits no fear in plummeting groundwards and swiping at the interloper. It even attacks humans – another reason why you can wait for pashas to find you rather than proactively search for them.

A tail on the hindwing is characteristic of many *Charaxes*. As its name suggests, the two-tailed pasha goes one better, having two such protrusions. These appear to serve twin purposes: to distract predators into attacking a non-essential part of the body, and warfare. The sharp points enable pugnacious males to slice at a rival's wings. Booze-fuelled bar brawl, anyone?

LARGE WHITE

Pieris brassicae

❖

WINGSPAN: *58–63mm (2¼–2½in)*
RANGE: *Europe, Africa, Asia*

Thanks to its caterpillars' taste for cultivated cabbages and other *Brassica* such as oilseed rape and kale, the large white is one of the world's most vilified butterflies. Yet it is also one of the most exceptional.

Commonly known as "cabbage white" – a name that also encompasses the small white (*Pieris rapae*) – this butterfly has been persecuted by gardeners and horticulturists for centuries. Scant regard is given to its subtle beauty – ivory-coloured with black spots and tips to the forewing and a deliciously smoky-yellow underside of the rear wing – or to its amazing lifestyle.

The large white is a remarkable migrant. Each summer, swarms routinely blizzard south from Scandinavia and the Baltic states into central

Europe. Its flight has been clocked at 16km/hour (10 miles/hour, three times human walking speed), and one "snowstorm" in 2011 comprised an astonishing six million butterflies snared on the sticky leaves of insectivorous plants called sundews in a single hectare of the Norfolk Broads, near the east coast of Britain.

The female large white lays clusters of yellow-orange eggs on the underside of *Brassica* leaves. As a consequence of the larval diet, these are impregnated with mustard oil to repel foragers. One enemy that is not daunted, however, is a parasitic wasp called *Trichogramma brassicae*. So tiny is this insect that 20 adults can grow within a single butterfly egg.

Large white eggs that hatch successfully have another trick up their sleeve. Thanks again to ingesting mustard oils, the caterpillars become poisonous. If a bird or shrew were to consume a large white caterpillar, its nervous system would become irritated and eventually collapse. In a further twist to the tale, certain wasps – one named *Cotesia glomeratus* – are immune to the effects of such chemicals, and routinely parasitize up to four-fifths of caterpillars.

MONARCH

Danaus plexippus

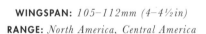

WINGSPAN: *105–112mm (4–4½in)*
RANGE: *North America, Central America*

In a forested grove on a Mexican mountainside, an entire tree is rustling. The source of the noise is not leaves, however, but butterflies – this is the winter roost of millions of monarchs. Every year since its 1975 discovery, the spectacle has enticed thousands of tourists to the Sierra Madre. As a result, monarchs have become one of the world's most widely recognized butterflies.

Monarchs start migrating south from boreal North America in September. Two main streams develop. The western blaze of orange settles in California, forming several hibernation roosts, each numbering tens of thousands. The eastern river of fire continues south into central Mexico.

The entire swarm concentrates into 10ha (25 acres) of forest across nine mountain tops where they almost entirely encrust favoured fir trees. In a good year, 175 million hibernating butterflies have been estimated. There is nothing else like this anywhere on Earth.

In mid-March, the same butterflies fly 3,600km (2,230 miles) north to breed. Few fully retrace their steps. Instead, the first wave procreates rapidly in the southern USA. The second generation heads north and repeats the process. The third brood reaches Canada in June, where it breeds in more leisurely fashion. It is thus the fourth generation of the year that makes the miraculous journey southwards.

How monarchs migrate, particularly how they navigate to the same few forest patches every autumn, perplexed biologists until recently. It had long been recognized that they navigate by the sun. But given that the sun's position in the sky moves between dawn and dusk, the monarchs must somehow adjust the information received to take account of the time of day. It transpires that their antennae serve this function. But precisely how they do so remains a mystery.

CELERIO SISTER

Adelpha serpa

- - -◆- - -

WINGSPAN: *47–54mm (1¾–2¼in)*
RANGE: *Central America, South America*

Blink and you will miss it. The celerio sister, in common with the other 80 members of the genus *Adelpha*, is a very fast flier. Indeed, fleeing rapidly is its primary defence against predation. Typically seen along the forest edge, it flies quickly, alights briefly on a leaf, then resumes airborne movement. In this behaviour, as well as its appearance, it recalls Eurasia's admirals (*Limenitis*).

Almost all the *Adelpha* sisters inhabit the New World Tropics. The celerio sister is one of the most widespread species, ranging from Mexico to Brazil. It is a rainforest insect, ascending mountain slopes to reach cloud forest as high as 2,000m (6,600ft).

Adelpha are remarkable in their similarity – exhibiting white and/or orange bands traversing marbled dark-brown wings. Accordingly, it is easy to recognize the genus – but much harder to determine which species you are watching. Indeed, many field guides and even museum specimens are erroneous. It took until 2001 for the genus to be properly deciphered by a British lepidopterist, Keith Wilmott, who determined that accurate identification was contingent on the precise configuration of orange markings and vertical bars on the upperwing.

It is not only butterfly-watchers who risk confusion. Given that many sisters not only resemble one another but also share the same habitat, how do insects know to mate with the right species? The poor resolution of the butterfly eye is inadequate to detect the minute physical differences between species, even at close range. If they were reliant on eyesight alone, male *Adelpha* butterflies would probably waste much of their short life chasing after a female of the wrong species. So some other cue must be at play – in this case, it is chemical messaging through the production and release of pheromones.

ZEBRA SWALLOWTAIL

Protographium marcellus

- - - ◆ - - -

WINGSPAN: *64–104mm (2½–4in)*
RANGE: *North America*

With translucent ivory wings, aggressively striped and shadowed ebony, and elongated sword-like tails at the back of these triangular wings, the zebra (or kite) swallowtail is a distinctive-looking creature. In eastern North America, this butterfly is also unique; its nearest relatives in the genus *Protographium* live in Central America, or further south into Bolivia.

You are most likely to see the zebra swallowtail winging its way purposefully through woodland bordering rivers or other damp terrain. It also seeks solace (well, nectar) in open, sunny areas nearby. Males patrol near food-plants in search of females, interrogating all vegetation below

human-head height. The female's most important responsibility is to locate a suitable pawpaw plant on which to lay an egg. So once a male finds good-looking pawpaws, it pays to hang around.

Sublime though the zebra swallowtail undeniably is, appearance is only one of its beguiling characteristics. Its life cycle abounds with fascinating quirks. Females lay a single egg on each selected leaf, to avoid the first-born cannibalizing its siblings. Unusually, the zebra swallowtail has two seasonal forms, one in spring and the other in summer. Early-flying swallowtails are smaller, paler and shorter-tailed than the later brood.

Adult butterflies, meanwhile, fuel their existence in very different ways. Females are typical of most butterflies, imbibing nectar from flowers. Males shun inflorescences, instead descending to the ground to mud-puddle, prioritizing salts and amino acids over sugars. In the absence of mud, mammal urine is more than adequate. It may sound antisocial, but some lepidopterists pee on a dry patch of soil and return the next day to see if a swallowtail has found their mineral-rich "offering".

COMMON BRIMSTONE

Gonepteryx rhamni

———— ◆ ————

WINGSPAN: *60–74mm (2⅓–3in)*
RANGE: *Europe, Asia, Africa*

It may be a familiar butterfly of scrubby woodland throughout Europe and Asia, but the common brimstone (usually simply known as brimstone) has some surprising claims to fame. It is thought to have been the very insect – the original "butter-coloured" fly – that accounts for the word "butterfly" in the English language.

Less well known is that brimstone is one of Europe's longest-lived butterflies. Adults typically survive 10 months (sometimes even a full year), even if they spend three-quarters of that time hibernating out of sight before emerging and preparing to breed. This is a remarkably hardy butterfly. In the north of its range, the brimstone is often the first butterfly to be seen airborne

each year. Sunny winter days temporarily coax males out of hibernation to power round in the crispness before the chill returns them to torpor.

Finally, the brimstone is notorious for being complicit in the first-recorded case of lepidopteran fraud. In 1702, a new species of butterfly was exhibited in Britain. This later transpired to simply be a brimstone that a butterfly-trader had painted with black and blue spots.

This butterfly's name reflects the male's vibrantly lemon coloration: "brimstone" is an old word for sulphur. Females are less intensely toned, being an insipid mint-yellow. Both have greener underwings designed for camouflage – the fundamental tool in a brimstone's survival kit. The female must avoid being munched by a bird while laying eggs, and both sexes need to survive the winter by hibernating amidst deciduous vegetation. Their angular wings firmly closed, brimstones look remarkably like leaves – even down to the skeletal venation.

COMMA

Polygonia c-album

------◆------

WINGSPAN: *50–64mm (2–2½in)*
RANGE: *Europe, Asia, Africa*

Snared on a hazel branch and surrounded by dangling lemony catkins, the desiccated, crumpled oak leaf looks out of place on a fine early-spring morning. Abruptly the leaf flurries into the air. It is no plant, but a golden-orange butterfly. The year's first comma is airborne.

From above, the comma is a blaze of a butterfly, but one so boldly spotted and banded as to prompt thought of a fritillary. With wings closed, however, it vanishes. On this doyen of camouflage, greys merge into beiges and become browns. A ragged outline convinces insectivorous birds that this is one leaf not worth investigating for hidden prey. There's even what appears to be a small hole mid-leaf: a

white comma-shaped mark from which the butterfly's vernacular name is derived.

Although primarily frequenting open, sunny woodland and forest edge, the comma regularly visits gardens, seduced by the prospect of ample nectar. It is thus a familiar butterfly across much of its range. But even the habitual can harbour surprises.

In the case of the comma, the revelation concerns its two-pronged survival strategy. The first caterpillars to develop in spring emerge as bright-golden adults. Butterflies that emerge later have a richer, tawny-red coloration. The first form – known as *hutchinsoni* after Emma Hutchinson, who first deciphered the comma's approach to life – breeds quickly, then dies within a few weeks. The second form, together with the offspring of the early-breeding *hutchinsoni*, hibernates through the winter, and is typically 10 months old before it mates and lays eggs. This system happens as a result of daylight length, spring temperatures and the degree of nutrition in leaves. It enables the comma to make the most of early springs and warm summers to squeeze more than one brood into a single year.

TEUCER OWL
BUTTERFLY

Caligo teucer

◆

WINGSPAN: *100–110mm (4–4¼in)*
RANGE: *South America, Central America*

The Teucer owl butterfly and its relatives explode the myth that all butterflies are sun-loving. These remarkable, mysterious creatures shun solar rays so intently that they only emerge from roost once the sun has set. Huge, lone individuals then flap clumsily through the South American rainforest, scant metres above ground, on the hunt for rotten fruit.

Such crepuscular behaviour – a strategy for minimizing encounters with diurnal predators – may be one reason why members of the genus

Caligo are known as owl butterflies. Other explanations are their feathery appearance and, most obviously, owl-like "eyes" adorning the underside of the hindwing.

The eyespots – or *ocelli* – are widely understood to enable the butterfly to mimic an owl, an appearance that would deter all but the most ambitious (or ill-advised) predator. This is certainly the case for other butterflies such as the peacock butterfly (*Inachis io*). But the theory breaks down quickly in relation to the Teucer owl butterfly, for only one side of its wings (and thus a single eyespot) is visible at any one time. Given that owls have two eyes, the butterfly is unlikely be pretending to be an owl.

A savvier rationale is that the eyespots act as decoys. The remainder of the underwing is cryptically patterned – swirled, barred and banded. This makes the butterfly hard for predators to spot within the shady Amazonian understorey – unless they watched the insect flop in ungainly fashion onto its perch. Approaching the butterfly, the insectivorous bird's focus will be on the eyespot, which lies in a non-critical part of the body. The bird may peck there, but the Teucer owl can still escape – damaged but alive.

RICINI LONGWING

Heliconius ricini

---◆---

WINGSPAN: *50−70mm (2−2¾in)*
RANGE: *Caribbean, South America*

A brightly coloured butterfly mesmerizes as it flutters delicately and painstakingly through the Guianan scrub. Its antennae are conspicuously long, and its wings have a distinctive, peculiar shape − long and slender, with rounded tips. They are largely black, but with a flaming base to the hindwing and eye-catching yellow stripes across the forewing.

"Eye-catching" is pertinent. The ricini longwing advertises its unpalatability, a legacy of its larvae having ingested a cyanide-like substance when nibbling on the fresh tendrils of passion vines (*Passiflora*). The New World tropics (Neotropics) host the vast majority of the world's 39 species of *Heliconius* longwings; all are toxic.

The ricini longwing differs from its genus norm in two ways. First, it inhabits savannah rather than dense tropical rainforest. Second, it has no other longwings with which it forms a "mimicry ring" (whereby two or more species benefit from mimicking each other's characteristics). In general, the genus *Heliconius* is a prime example of what has become known as "Müllerian mimicry". Biologist Fritz Müller studied groups of near-identical butterflies comprising different species, and found that, rather than these consisting of a benign species defending itself by mimicking a toxic one (Batesian mimicry), all were toxic. Müller theorized that there was safety in numbers: the more species that look similar, the more pervasive the message of unpalatability and the less likely any individuals of those species are to be eaten. Many longwings produce different colour forms, each of which is a dead ringer for another species in the genus.

One way in which the ricini longwing does fit typical *Heliconius* behaviour is in the male's mating strategy. A day before emerging from her pupa as an adult butterfly, the female is thought to emit pheromones that indicate her whereabouts to males. The first male to locate the female sits guard atop the pupa, and mates with her the following morning as she crawls out of the chrysalis.

SCARCE SWALLOWTAIL

Iphiclides podalirius

❖

WINGSPAN: *65–80mm (2½–3¼in)*
RANGE: *Europe, Asia*

In the midday heat on a dry, rocky Mediterranean hillside, a gentle exhalation of wind billows into the air an exquisitely patterned pastel-yellow triangle. The scarce swallowtail sails the current, floating an arc from an apple tree towards the next blossom-laden target. Tiger-striped with streamers for tails and red-rimmed blue "eyes" adorning its hindwings, there are few finer butterflies throughout the whole of Europe and Asia.

Despite its common name, this butterfly is neither absolutely scarce (although recent habitat change seems to be rendering it less common) nor relatively so (it is the most common and widespread of the trio of species in the genus *Iphiclides*). The moniker reflects the (understandable)

parochialism of eighteenth-century British lepidopterists. The species is an occasional visitor to Britain, so was simply scarce in comparison to the native swallowtail (*Papilio machaon*), which is shorter-tailed, brighter yellow and more densely chequered with black.

Until recently, it was thought that Europe hosted just a single species of *Iphiclides* swallowtail, gliding and swooping around meadows, parks and scrubland. Alerted by slight but consistent differences in the pattern and coloration of supposed scarce swallowtails south of the Pyrenees, butterfly experts took a closer look. And I really mean *close*. Careful examination of characteristics not visible to the naked human eye – the precise shape of genitalia and small but significant differences in mitochondrial DNA – confirmed suspicions that a separate species was involved: southern scarce swallowtail (*Iphiclides feisthamelii*). We have so much to learn – even about common butterflies in well-studied parts of the world.

VARIABLE CRACKER

Hamadryas feronia

❮─────◆─────❯

WINGSPAN: *70–86mm (2¾–3½in)*
RANGE: *North, Central and South America*

Few butterflies shock quite like the variable cracker (*Hamadryas*). With its ocellated, marbled and stippled upperwings, it blends impressively with the tree trunk on which it is perched, wings spread and head facing downwards. Such camouflage makes it easy to overlook – and that is the intention, at least as far as predators are concerned. Little wonder humans are startled by the loud, sharp noise that the male cracker produces as he flies at them, apparently enraged that they have intruded on his territory.

Butterflies are well known for their looks, and increasingly for their smells (the pheromones emitted to facilitate mating). But unlike insects such as

cicadas and grasshoppers, it is very rare for a butterfly to produce sounds. Granted, some butterflies produce incidental noise, such as the rustling of wings. And the peacock butterfly (*Inachis io*) rubs together its wings to "hiss" at predators. But the noise produced by the variable cracker (also known as blue or Feronia cracker) and its woodland-dwelling New World relatives is utterly different.

The twanging, whipcrack-like sounds are produced by the male only, by repeatedly striking together two hollow veins in its forewings. Whereas the peacock's hissing is directed towards predators, the cracker's noise is intended for other individuals of its own species.

We know this because the cracker, again very unusually among butterflies, possesses what passes for an "ear" at the base of the underwing. This funnel-shaped sac, covered by a thin membrane that vibrates in response to particular sounds, communicates messages to the brain. The purpose of the sound is improperly understood, but may be twofold. If given towards another male, territorial conflict ensues. If the sound is produced upon the arrival of a female, the male moves into courtship mode.

DIRCE BEAUTY

Colobura dirce

------ ◆ ------

WINGSPAN: *c.33mm (1¼in)*
RANGE: *South America, Central America, Caribbean*

Talk about hiding in plain sight. For more than 200 years, the Dirce beauty has been admired as one of the most common and widespread butterflies in the Neotropics. It resides in rainforests from Mexico to Argentina, from sea-level to the Andean foothills. It is readily found around human habitation, being particularly attracted to decomposing fruit and vegetables.

Yet at the start of this millennium, diligent lepidopterists determined that "Dirce beauty" was actually two separate species. The previously undiscovered butterfly, given the name annulata beauty, had been there all along – but nobody had looked closely enough at a familiar butterfly

to detect its cryptic counterpart.

To be fair, the new species's differences were slight. Annulata beauty caterpillars are encircled by yellow rings. Adults are marginally larger, with slightly divergent patterning on the strikingly zebra-striped underwing. Scientists then unravelled disparities in the duo's biology. Aggregations of Dirce beauty larvae were smaller than those of annulata beauty. This appeared to correlate with the age of the cecropia tree on which females lay their eggs. The annulata beauty oviposits in the canopy of mature trees, where ample food can support numerous offspring. In contrast, the Dirce beauty female lays eggs on saplings (even seedlings); with little leaf available, numbers of offspring are necessarily lower.

Despite these differences, the two beauties share a common enemy. Slap a cecropia tree, and ants of the genus *Azteca* emerge from its hollow trunk to attack you. The ants live symbiotically with the tree, which provides nutritious packets of food in exchange for protection from herbivores bent on eating cecropia leaves. *Colobura* caterpillars, however, have a trick up their larval sleeve: they secrete a noxious substance that repels the hymenopteran defenders. Even for creatures living in plain sight, there is plenty more to the beauties than meets the eye.

CLIO CRESCENT

Eresia clio

─── ─── ◆ ─── ───

WINGSPAN: *c.36mm (1½in)*
RANGE: *Central America, South America*

Along the edge of many Neotropical forests between Mexico and Bolivia, there is a good chance of encountering a swarm of clio crescents. This common butterfly frequents scrubby lowland areas adjoining forest; being a sun-lover, it shuns the shady interior. Adults feed on flower nectar, but only males descend to damp ground to replenish minerals lost during copulation.

Fluttering delicately on long, rounded black wings marked by ivory splodges and broad bars, there is something of a longwing (*Heliconius* or *Eueides*) in the crescent's demeanour. There is indeed a link between the crescent's genus (*Eresia*) and *Eueides* longwings – but it is rather more

explicit in the clio crescent's sister species.

Whereas several *Eresia* follow the basic black-and-white colour pattern of the clio crescent, others are strongly patterned in black and orange. The latter are fraudsters, pretending to be toxic types of longwing – another example of Batesian mimicry. (A nineteenth-century British explorer and naturalist, Henry Bates gathered evidence for his theory during a four-year expedition to Amazonia. Fathoming the relationship between *Eueides* and lookalike *Eresia* was critical to his success.)

For such a familiar, relatively abundant and undeniably widespread butterfly, surprisingly little is known about the ecology of the clio crescent. If it is similar to other species in the genus, which have benefited from a modicum of study, females may lay a few score eggs in a single batch below the leaves of a nettle-like shrub (*Pilea*). That we have to extrapolate the lifestyle of even a familiar butterfly offers stern counsel about destroying the global environment when we have barely started to understand it.

MALAY BIRDWING

Troides amphrysus

– – – ◆ – – –

WINGSPAN: *150–180mm (6–7in)*
RANGE: *Asia*

Even across a rainforest clearing, a flickering at an orange umbel of a lantana bush catches the visitor's eye. Viewed closer, it becomes evident that the movement is the frantic pumping of the wings of a butterfly the size of a human hand. One disadvantage of being so gargantuan is that the Malay birdwing is physically unable to perch on a plant while feeding. Such a pose may be standard behaviour for most butterflies, but Malay birdwings are not most butterflies. So heavy is this butterfly's body that it must flutter rapidly while it dips its proboscis into nectar.

The Malay birdwing is very similar in appearance to the common birdwing (*Troides helena*) but lacks the latter's fiery crimson spots on the head

and thorax. The range of the Malay birdwing is wholly contained within that of the much more widespread common birdwing, occurring from Myanmar to Indonesia via Peninsular Malaysia. Like its sister species, the Malay birdwing is a butterfly of the tropical rainforest.

Male and female Malay birdwings differ slightly from one another. Flashes in the forewing are yellow in the male but white in the female. The male's hindwings are a brighter yellow, with sporadic black dots restricted to the rear border, quite unlike the female's extensively dark hindwing.

Any ground-level sighting is likely to take place in the afternoon. Malay birdwing mornings are dedicated to courtship, in the forest canopy, about 20m (66ft) overhead. Flashes of gold suggest a male birdwing circling a female concealed by a verdant shroud. Should the male find the female, he will hover above her, fanning pheromones her way, seeking to persuade her to mix their genes.

BANDED LONGWING

Dryadula phaetusa

──── ◆ ────

WINGSPAN: *86–89mm (3¼–3½in)*
RANGE: *South America*

A banded longwing is an insect of two halves. Its eye-catching upperwing is tiger-striped – flaming orange with dark-brown cross-bands. The underside is no less beautiful, but clearly designed to avoid attracting attention: largely brown, with white stripes edged in orange – a pattern perfect for concealing the butterfly in the fading light of the rainforest day. The interplay of ebbing sun and growing shadow finds its echo in the underwing of the butterflies as they roost gregariously, upside down, clinging to the underside of a leaf.

The banded longwing, also known variously as banded orange heliconian, orange tiger and banded orange, is taxonomically unique. It is

the only member of a genus (*Dryadula*) that slots into the wider "tribe" of Heliconiini, collectively known as longwings. Like other members of the tribe, the banded longwing is dependent on passion vines for its survival, as these are the caterpillar's food-plant.

Ranging from Brazil north to Mexico, the banded longwing favours disturbed locations in forests, whether roads, clearings or riverbanks. Both sexes visit flowers such as lantana and milkweeds to consume nectar. Males also stock up on salts during the breeding season by drinking from muddy puddles or even from the hide of some animals.

As well as patrolling actively, males "own" prominent perches from which they scan the environs for signs of a female. Should the male encounter one, he pursues her until she acquiesces and settles on shady ground. The male then courts favour, performing a figure-of-eight display before settling beside her. The female indicates her receptiveness by remaining motionless. Half-opening his wings, the male wafts pheromones towards her. All being well, mating ensues, and the female departs in search of a passion vine on which to produce the next generation of banded longwings.

MAP BUTTERFLY

Arashnia   levana

--- --- ◆ --- ---

WINGSPAN: *30–46mm (1¼–1¾in)*
RANGE: *Asia, Europe*

Most butterflies lay their eggs singly, but some oviposit (to use the entomological term) in batches. The latter strategy minimizes the energy involved in searching for suitable egg-laying sites and enables the female to lay as many as possible before being nabbed by a predator. But it has downsides too: all the female's eggs sit in a single metaphorical basket. A few species, including the map butterfly, fellow members of the genus *Arashnia* and commas (*Polygonia*), adopt a third strategy. The females lay eggs one atop the other, in a vertical strand that dangles from the underside of a leaf; in the case of the map, this is usually a stinging nettle. Why they do this – and with what outcome – is presently unknown.

Most members of the *Arashnia* reside in east Asia, but the map also ranges west into temperate Europe. Here it frequents clearings in deciduous woodland and bushy scrub. Like many species of butterfly, it raises two generations in a single season; in the map's case, however, unlike most other species, the two broods look utterly different from one another.

The spring brood (*levana*; typically on the wing in May/June) recalls a fritillary or small tortoiseshell (*Aglais urticae*), being boldly patterned orange and black, with a blue rear border and white dots on the forewing. The offspring of this brood, known as *prorsa*, hatch from late July to early September. Not only are they 10 per cent larger, but they also recall a bonsai poplar admiral (*Limenitis populi*), being largely black with white bands. So marked are the differences between the broods that it is hard to imagine that they belong to the same species... until you see the underwing. The intricate pattern of deep chestnut, scarlet, ivory and black is very similar regardless of when the map is born.

BLUE-LEAF PANSY

Junonia cymodoce

---◆---

WINGSPAN: *100–110mm (4–4¼in)*
RANGE: *Africa*

Midday in a Central African rainforest. The heat stifles, the humidity oppresses, yet far more awe-inspiring is the winged jewel of a sizeable blue-leaf pansy, perched on a wide leaf, head pointing towards the ground and wings held flat.

Two features on this tropical butterfly catch the eye. The first is a substantial blue tract on the upperwing that glints dramatically. The colour is not pigmentation but the interplay of sun on complex microscopic wing structures. This butterfly aims to attract the attention of members of its own species.

The upward curve of the wing draws the gaze to the second striking

characteristic. At the base of each hindwing is a staring eye. With its white-rimmed dark pupil and even a "catchlight", it resembles a living animal. By the look of the "snout" generated by the nose-like tip to the butterfly's abdomen, it could even be a carnivorous mammal. This butterfly seeks to persuade predators that they themselves are in danger of being eaten.

Each wing is remarkably similar in shape to the leaf on which the butterfly sits: both hindwing and forewing taper to a narrow point. Were the butterfly to lift its wings, it would merge into the ageing vegetation, for its underwing form and coloration (various dingy shades of brown) make it a dead ringer for a decaying leaf.

The blue-leaf pansy is one of just two African members of the genus *Junonia*, which also includes the buckeyes. In shape and coloration, pansy and buckeye are strikingly different. Can they really be members of the same genus? Lepidopterists are starting to ask whether the African pair should be granted their own genus, *Kamilla*.

LARGE
TORTOISESHELL

Nymphalis polychloros

- - - ◆ - - -

WINGSPAN: *68–75mm (2⅔–3in)*
RANGE: *Europe, Africa, Asia*

Woe betide any blue tit that chances upon a dingy grey web serving as the collective home of a hundred large tortoiseshell caterpillars. The youngsters – instars, in entomologist-speak – are intently stripping fresh leaves from the uppermost branches of a wych elm (*Ulmus glabra*) or sallow (*Salix* sp). And they are loath to be disturbed.

Each caterpillar is sheathed in tiny spines capable of piercing avian skin. If that were not deterrent enough, disturbance by a predator prompts the siblings to simultaneously jerk their bodies – so that the entire web

suddenly seethes with spines. The blue tit does well to leave them alone.

When its gestation is complete in July or August, the adult large tortoiseshell unfurls its hefty amber wings and prepares for action. But after a fortnight of activity, at most, it is ready for a protracted period of inaction – and hibernates for seven or so months until early spring.

Large tortoiseshells schedule their subsequent awakening for the flowering of goat willow (*Salix cinerea*). Energy boost complete, the adults fly widely through wooded countryside, mating when the opportunity arises and laying eggs wherever there is suitable habitat.

Although strikingly similar in appearance to the small tortoiseshell (*Aglais urticae*), one of Europe's most common and best-known butterflies, the large tortoiseshell is only distantly related. It belongs to a different genus – alongside, counter-intuitively, mourning cloak (aka Camberwell beauty, *Nymphalis antiopa*), which looks very different indeed.

The large tortoiseshell is common across much of its range, with the current exception of the UK. In 1901, it was "excessively abundant in north Essex" according to one Victorian collector. But by the 1950s it was extinct – possibly as a result of Dutch elm disease which devastated an important larval food-plant.

MADAGASCAR GIANT SWALLOWTAIL

Pharmacophagus antenor

- - - ◆ - - -

WINGSPAN: *120–140mm (4¾–5½in)*
RANGE: *Africa*

How can something so striking, beautiful and unmistakable be so mysterious, anomalous and inexplicable? In a country renowned for the diversity of life forms that have radiated from single original ancestors – think lemurs and chameleons – the Madagascar giant swallowtail stands proud as an exception.

As the butterfly tacks high through the air, from the canopy of one emergent tree to another, its mighty size and unrepentantly spotted wings captivate. This is a yacht's sail in lepidopteran form. As it deigns to descend to your level, you

observe finer detail that renders the creature even more exquisite: bulging, glistening blue hindwings blinking with crimson half-moons, a scarlet head and antennae and an abdomen striped candy-pink and white.

But there is a problem. The Madagascar giant swallowtail is in the wrong place. It is the only Afrotropical member of a tribe of butterflies called the Troidini, the pipevine swallowtails – so named because their caterpillars feed exclusively on pipevines (*Aristolochia*). The Madagascar giant swallowtail's nearest relatives are the birdwings of Asia and Australasia, thousands of miles away across the Indian and Pacific Oceans. So unexpected was the giant swallowtail's home that it took a full century after its discovery (when its location was unspecified) for lepidopterists to realize that it occurred on, and indeed was wholly restricted to, Madagascar. How it reached there has never been satisfactorily explained.

Liberated from closely related competitors, this swallowtail has been able to adapt its life cycle to particular local conditions across the world's fourth-largest island. In drier areas, for example, the pupa suspends its development when deciduous trees shed their leaves. When the year's rains arrive, it restarts its progress towards adulthood. What other secrets will eventually be imparted by this fascinating outlier of the swallowtails?

POPLAR ADMIRAL

Limenitis populi

———◆———

WINGSPAN: *72–96mm (2¾–3¾in)*
RANGE: *Europe, Asia*

It may not quite have the allure of a purple emperor (*Apatura iris*), but the poplar admiral comes very close indeed. The admiral is marginally larger than the emperor – with females similarly dwarfing males – and similarly patterned. Sadly, the male admiral lacks the emperor's opulent purple upperwing, having at best a blue sheen. The admiral nudges it on the underwing, however, being more extensively fiery orange.

Although not particularly closely related – being in different subfamilies within the same family – the two butterflies exhibit similarities in ecology as well as appearance. Both inhabit mature deciduous woodland and fly majestically with glides and swoops. Both have an unseemly fascination

for smelly substances ranging from carnivore excrement to human sweat, and from petrol to melting tar. Males of both species are easier to see than females – indeed, encountering a female poplar admiral would be a red-letter day for a butterfly-watcher.

Clearly, though, there are marked differences – as you would expect for two species that share only a very distant ancestor. The poplar admiral lacks the pronounced "eye" exhibited by the purple emperor on both its upper- and underwing. The poplar admiral is associated with black poplar (*Populus nigra*) and aspen (*Populus tremula*) trees, which are the sole food-plants of its caterpillars. You would never catch a purple emperor on either of these trees, its preference being for sallow (*Salix*), so the pair rarely occur at the same site. Even the caterpillars have small but significant differences in lifestyle. Admiral larvae eat the leaf tip of their food-plants (an extremity shunned by emperor caterpillars), and spend the winter in a *hibernaculum* they have formed from a partially eaten leaf.

EASTERN TIGER
SWALLOWTAIL

Papilio glaucus

----◆----

WINGSPAN: *79–140mm (3–5½in)*
RANGE: *North America*

Beneath a scorching sun, a lemon squabble of male eastern tiger swallowtails jostle at an unexpected puddle on the otherwise dried-out Texan roadside, all needing to replenish minerals lost during courtship. Once sated, each butterfly departs, resuming his quest for virgin females.

Boldly striped and emphatically tailed, the eastern tiger swallowtail is among eastern North America's most striking, familiar and common butterflies. Not only is it long loved – the subject of the first-known illustration of a North American butterfly, back in 1587 – but it is also much

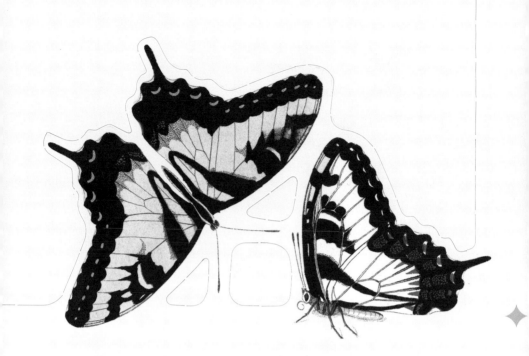

loved: the state butterfly or state insect of six US Senate jurisdictions. Yet despite such appreciation, this swallowtail brings surprises and secrets.

Its taxonomy continues to perplex. Although long housed in the genus *Papilio*, some taxonomists place the tiger swallowtail in its own grouping, *Pterourus*. Moreover, "tiger swallowtail" was traditionally considered a single species with a vast North American range, but research in recent decades has revealed that four species are actually involved, hence the "birth" of the *eastern* tiger swallowtail, which is restricted to central and eastern US states.

The size spectrum for this butterfly reveals that, unusually, the largest individual is nearly double the size of the smallest. There are three reasons for this. Southern populations are bigger than northern; females heftier than males; and first broods are dwarfed by subsequent ones.

There are also quirks in this swallowtail's appearance. In the southern part of its range, some female eastern tigers are wholly bluish-black rather than yellow. This is because they seek to evade predation by mimicking a local toxic butterfly, the pipevine swallowtail (*Battus philenor*). Even more intriguingly, the eastern tiger swallowtail is one of few butterflies worldwide that includes individuals with one male wing and one female wing ("bilateral gynandromorphs"). Sometimes even the most familiar creature can be unfamiliar.

TIGER LEAFWING

Consul fabius

--- ◆ ---

WINGSPAN: *30–35mm (1¼–1½in)*
RANGE: *South America, Central America*

Across the world, caterpillar survival strategies vary markedly. Some larvae thwart predators by being toxic, camouflaged or scary-looking. Some (including the peacock butterfly, *Inachis io*) live communally within large silk shelters. Others, such as the tiger leafwing, follow a solitary existence in individual bivouacs. The caterpillar wraps itself tightly in a leaf, then "plugs" the entrance with its head, which is hardened to prevent piercing by parasitic wasps. Such an imaginative approach to survival continues into adulthood.

In its mature stage of life, the tiger leafwing (or tiger-with-tails) minimizes the prospects of becoming lunch by deploying not one but three

strategies. Basking in the sun, wings held open, the vibrant orange, yellow and black coloration (hence "tiger") implies that the species is too toxic to eat. In reality, tiger-with-tails is a Batesian mimic, an impostor disguising its palatability by imitating the coloration of genuinely noxious butterflies. With its wings snapped shut, the reason for the other half of the butterfly's name (leafwing) becomes apparent. Variegated buff, brown and magenta underwings perfectly mimic a shrivelled leaf, thus blending the form into its woodland domain. Should either approach fail, the predator's attention is likely to be drawn to the protruding tail at the rear of each wing; if the bird pecks at that, there's no substantive harm done.

To see this common inhabitant of sunny edges, glades and thoroughfares in rainforests from Mexico to Bolivia, one approach is to climb up a canopy tower at a rainforest lodge. Males spend much of the day basking in the uppermost foliage, surveying their leafy domain from an elevated position. Should you lack a head for heights, don't fret. Around midday, females that have mated glide slowly to the understorey, where they flit between shrubs suitable for egg-laying. Both sexes also feast on fruit that slowly decomposes on the forest floor.

PARIS PEACOCK

Papilio paris

---◆---

WINGSPAN: *106–130mm (4¼–5in)*
RANGE: *Asia*

A shadow floats beneath the Thai rainforest canopy, gently but deliberately descending towards a generously flowered citrus tree. It turns out to be a densely black butterfly with broad, rounded wings and spoons for tails. As the mighty insect hovers frantically to maintain its feeding position, it reveals phosphorescence peppering its upperwing. Formally known as "irroration", this sparkling-green dusting is common to a mere handful of swallowtail species. The Paris peacock is the most common and widespread member of this select band, ranging through lowland rainforests from India through Southeast Asia and Indonesia to China.

Living in rainforests confers several advantages on the Paris peacock and other tropical butterflies. Seasons are less pronounced than in temperate regions; relatively consistent temperatures allow continuous breeding rather than enforcing an annual cycle into which butterflies must cram one or two broods. The same climatic characteristics mean a similarly unending succession of flowering plants. Wherever it lives, an adult Paris peacock will always find nectar on which to feed and its caterpillars will always have suitable leaves to nibble.

Even judging by the eight species covered in this book, *Papilio* swallowtails appear to be a diverse group, exhibiting marked variety in colour and pattern. It is slightly surprising that all 200 or so *Papilio* worldwide are considered to belong to the same genus. But this analysis represents a considerable refinement of the original classification. In the eighteenth century, *all* butterflies were thought to belong a single genus – *Papilio*. Understanding of the evolutionary relationships between different butterflies has greatly improved since those days!

DRAGON SWALLOWTAIL

Sericinus montela

---◆------

WINGSPAN: *50–90mm (2–3½in)*
RANGE: *Asia*

A miniature white kite gusts over a rock-strewn valley slope in eastern China, its elongated, snowy streamers trailing wistfully behind. Even among a famously beautiful butterfly family (Papilionidae, the swallowtails), the dragon swallowtail is jaw-droppingly sublime. The sole member of its genus, it is truly one of a kind. The male's wings recall the sumptuous mountain Apollo (*Parnassius apollo*); the female's are uncompromisingly blotched black. Both sexes celebrate a preposterously long tail – three times that of a typical swallowtail.

Such a dramatic-looking creature has caught the attention of scientists across its range in the Russian Far East, China and Korea. Some have discovered that the dragon swallowtail is the only member of its sub-family (Parnassiinae) capable of breeding more than once a year. Others have revealed that the warmer the season, the quicker the dragon swallowtail completes its life cycle. With ambient temperatures of 30°C (86°F), males take just a fortnight to develop from egg to adult – four times quicker than at 15°C (60°F). Lepidopterists have also shown that the closer to the equator a dragon swallowtail population lives, the smaller and darker it is.

Unmistakable though the dragon swallowtail is, the species had a confused early existence. Its eighteenth-century discoverer named it *Papilio telamon*. This posed a problem, because that moniker had already been allocated to another butterfly. It took a century before things were smoothed out by simply inverting the scientific name such that *telamon* became *montela*.

Unfortunately, there is an invidious dimension to the dragon swallowtail. The species occurs in Japan only as a result of an illicit or unintentional introduction. In fear that this "invasive alien species" will outcompete a native butterfly, the Chinese windmill (*Byasa alcinous*), Japanese authorities have designated the dragon as a pest. Even beauty is unwelcome if it is in the wrong place.

RED-SPOTTED
PURPLE
(or AMERICAN WHITE ADMIRAL)
Limenitis arthemis

◆-------

WINGSPAN: *47–78mm (1¾–3in)*
RANGE: *North America*

One butterfly or two? It has two names and two very different-looking forms, yet the red-spotted purple (aka American white admiral) has astonished lepidopterists by proving to be the very same species, inhabiting sunny clearings in North America's deciduous woodland.

Illustrated above, the American white admiral (subspecies *arthemis* and *rubrofasciata*) frequents northeastern North America. As is typical

of the genus *Limenitis* (see poplar admiral, *Limenitis populi*), its purplish-brown upperwing is broadly banded with white. The red-spotted purple (subspecies *astyanax*) resides mainly in the southern USA. Its upperwing lacks the northern relative's white bands, with both faces of the wing instead exhibiting crimson dots atop a sumptuous metallic-blue sheen.

Why such difference? It transpires that the red-spotted purple (but not the American white admiral) mimics the pipevine swallowtail (*Battus philenor*), a noxious species. Imitation is only valuable where the two species overlap – which is solely where the purple lives, and not the admiral. The latter's protection strategy involves disruptive coloration – the broad white band breaking up its form.

But nature is rarely neatly cut-and-dried. Occasional purples with a white band are seen in the northern part of its range. The odd admiral lacking white bands is sometimes found in the range of purples. Both quirks are the result of recessive genes, and – together with the fertile offspring produced through hybridization – confirm that the two forms pertain to the same species. This is one of the most remarkable examples of mixed pairings between mimetic and non-mimetic individuals.

PIPEVINE
SWALLOWTAIL

Battus philenor

--- --- ◆ --- ---

WINGSPAN: *70–130mm (2¾–5in)*
RANGE: *North America, Central America*

Easily disturbed, a male pipevine swallowtail swirls upwards from the sodden mud where it has procured a gift integral to successful courtship. Knowing that females lay their eggs on pipevines (*Aristolochia*), the blue-black butterfly makes haste to a suitable plant of that species. When he spots a female arrive, the male flashes iridescent blue hindwings, the "quality" of which somehow communicates to the female his suitability as a mate. Should the female be persuaded to copulate, the male conveys his gratitude by passing her the sodium

that he extracted from the damp, mineral-rich ground earlier in the day.

As its common name suggests, pipevines are critical to this butterfly's survival strategy. Its caterpillars feed solely on *Aristolochia* leaves, ingesting acids that render them poisonous throughout their life. Both caterpillars and adults provide potential predators with an unequivocal visual warning of their toxicity by being patterned with bright orange-red spots.

Several harmless species of butterfly have cottoned onto this and, as adults, seek protection from predators by mimicking the appearance of the pipevine swallowtail. Two of these Batesian mimics are featured in this book: the eastern tiger swallowtail (*Papilio glaucus*) and the red-spotted purple or American white admiral (*Limenitis arthemis*).

Not all predators are deterred by the pipevine swallowtail's appearance. Their warning may function for birds, which shun the butterflies, but it doesn't work for small lizards called anoles. Biologists in Texas have watched these lizards catch, chew and swallow pipevine swallowtails without any obvious adverse effect. One hypothesis is that the lizards have evolved to tolerate or even detoxify the noxious aristolochian acids that permeate the butterfly.

CRIMSON TIP

Colotis danae

WINGSPAN: *45–52mm (1¾–2in)*
RANGE: *Africa, Asia*

It's best not to look for the crimson tip during the heat of the day. When the sun shines brightly, this small butterfly is incessantly active – fuelled by solar energy and sugar-rich nectar. Save your search for either end of the day, when these attractive butterflies are becalmed by the cooler air. At such times, they rest placidly with their wings half open (a trademark of the genus *Colotis*), harnessing whatever warmth they can.

The crimson tip (also known as scarlet tip) is one of 40 members in its genus, which is part of the whites family (Pieridae). Like all bar one of its "congeners", it inhabits tropical Africa, where it ranges widely

from Gambia to Ethiopia, then south to South Africa. It is also part of a select bunch among the African *Colotis* whose distributions extend into the Indian subcontinent.

In appearance, the crimson tip is typical of the genus. It is essentially white with brightly coloured tips to the forewing – in this case, as its name suggests, carmine. Females are distinguished from males by being stippled with black. The residual *Colotis* differ markedly by having largely yellow upperwings that are smoked with charcoal grey.

This is a butterfly of open, scrubby areas such as Acacia-infused savannah. The crimson tip's entire life cycle is inseparable from shrubs of the genus *Cadaba*, which are in the caper family (Capparaceae). Rather unusually among butterflies, adults commonly imbibe nectar at flowers of the same plant whose leaves nourished them as caterpillars.

COMMON LIME
BUTTERFLY

Papilio demoleus

❖

WINGSPAN: *65–100mm (2½–4in)*
RANGE: *Middle East, Asia, Australasia, Caribbean, Central America*

Everybody, everywhere, loves butterflies, right? Not quite. Beautiful
though the common lime butterfly may be, it incurs the hatred
of horticulturalists with an economic stake in the citrus market. The
caterpillars of common lime – also known variously as lemon butterfly,
lime swallowtail and, less provocatively, chequered swallowtail – are
voracious consumers of the leaves of lemon and lime trees, able to
completely defoliate saplings and devastate entire nurseries or orchards.
Breeding intensively and flying powerfully, common lime populations

can spread rapidly along corridors of citrus plantations.

Until recently, common lime butterfly was exclusively an Old World "problem", as it ranged across Asia, Australasia and the Middle East. But it has now reached the New World too, having been inadvertently introduced to the Caribbean. Growers of citrus trees do not take the invasion lying down. Many use biopesticides that seek to destroy the "pest", ostensibly without damaging the wider environment. Others deploy natural pest control, introducing parasitic yellow wasps (*Polistes hebreus*) or a predatory Indian flower mantis (*Creobrator gemmatus*).

All of which, from a butterfly-lover's perspective, is a crying shame. The common lime is one of the world's most stunning swallowtails. Although it lacks the protrusions from the hindwing for which these butterflies are named, it has gloriously chequered upperwings and an even more sumptuous underwing that complements a tangerine suffusion with black, white and crimson markings. A gathering of 20 or more males at a tiny muddy puddle is a sight that takes some beating.

COMMON OLIVEWING

Nessaea aglaura

━ ━ ━ ◆ ━ ━ ━

WINGSPAN: *28–36mm (1–1½in)*
RANGE: *Central America, South America*

In the humid Costa Rican tropical forest, dripping and perpetually verdant, a tiny splash of brilliant blue catches the eye. A small butterfly has paused on a leaf, opening its wings flat to reveal neon bands upon otherwise black upperwings. Suddenly, the insect disappears, then part of the leaf takes to the air and shoots rapidly out of sight. The butterfly had not, it transpires, moved from the leaf, but blended in with it.

The initial disappearing act of this common olivewing (or of its three fellow members of the genus *Nessaea*, which collectively range through the Neotropics from Mexico to Argentina) was due to its leaf-green underwings providing perfect camouflage in the rainforest. The butterfly remained

on the leaf, but the slightest movement startled this wary creature into snapping shut its wings.

Given how successful the olivewing is, it is rather surprising that more butterflies have not evolved apple-green wings. The olivewing is even more unusual because the green and blue colours it exhibits are derived from true pigmentation. These two colours, plus purple, are usually produced structurally – by tiny physical structures that interact with or diffract light. The iridescent cyan-green of the common banded peacock (*Papilio crino*), the electric flash of the sickle-winged morpho (*Morpho rhetenor*) and the metallic-blue sheen of the red-spotted purple or American white admiral (*Limenitis arthemis*) are all examples of structural coloration. With its genuine blue and green pigment – more like emulsion paint than reflective tints – the olivewing is truly a special butterfly.

TAMIL LACEWING

Cethosia nietneri

WINGSPAN: *80–100mm (3¼–4in)*
RANGE: *Asia*

With their intricately embroidered underwings, lacewings (*Cethosia*) are among the most beautiful butterflies in Asia and Australasia. But the slip-stitches, crochets, eyelets and chevrons are not merely for embellishment: they are for survival. Both underwing and upperwing on the Tamil lacewing serve as a disruptive pattern, duping would-be predators into believing that they imagined a butterfly form. In lacewings, splendour is secondary to staying alive.

Depending on whose taxonomy takes precedence, there are between 13 and 17 species of lacewing distributed from India through Southeast Asia and the Pacific to Australia. Oddly, their closest relatives are in a

different continent – Central and South America. Lacewings are part of the longwing tribe (Heliconiini), whose famous members include the genus *Heliconius*.

Lacewings tend to prefer open, forested habitats such as village gardens near woodland. Most active in the morning, they are usually encountered singly with wings held half open as they imbibe nectar from a flowering plant. When the butterfly takes off, its flight is initially laborious, but gathers momentum as it ascends.

As its name suggests, the Tamil (or Ceylon) lacewing is mainly found in the tropical forests of Sri Lanka, where it is one of 250 species of butterflies recorded. Its range extends onto the Indian subcontinent, where it occurs in the Western Ghats. Flying from the onset of the monsoon (usually June) until September, the Tamil lacewing occurs throughout Sri Lanka up to 1,200m (4,000ft) altitude, but is most frequent at mid-elevation (600–900m; 2,000–3,000ft). Nevertheless, it is rarely common – which makes it a much-sought-after species for the increasing numbers of people visiting Sri Lanka on butterfly-watching tours.

FELIX'S HAIRSTREAK

Evenus felix

— — — ◆ — — —

WINGSPAN: *44–64mm (1¾–2½in)*
RANGE: *Central America, South America*

How little we know about the world in which we live. And how little time may remain for us to come to know, given the rate at which we are destroying and degrading it. Had I penned this book as recently as 2013, I would have been writing this particular text about a butterfly called the crowned hairstreak (*Evenus coronata*). In 2014, however, two lepidopterists played detective, visiting a collection of butterfly specimens held by a Venezuelan family. Examining the mounted butterflies with excruciating care, they confirmed the family's hunch that "crowned hairstreak" was not one species but two.

The differences are small – in some cases, minute – but unequivocal.

In the illustration above, the size of the red spots on the hindwing decree that this particular butterfly is the new, previously undiscovered, species: Felix's hairstreak. A female crowned hairstreak would exhibit more extensive black borders to smaller crimson spots. Remarkably, it transpires that Felix's hairstreak is actually the commoner of the two species – and the one for which the Ecuadorian town of Baños has become famous for exporting from its butterfly farms.

Even without such revelations, *Evenus* hairstreaks are amazing butterflies. Their shimmering blue upperwing and metallic green underwing are both the result of "structural coloration" (the movement of light around tiny ridges and furrows on the wing scales). But arguably the most intriguing feature of the hairstreaks, as intimated by the name, is the wispy double "tail" that protrudes from the back of the hindwing. These are mock antennae, designed to trick predators into thinking that the back of the butterfly is its head. An insectivorous bird is thus more likely to peck at the rear of the insect, allowing it to zip into the air and wing away to safety with its important body parts intact.

BRIMSTONE WING

Hebomoia leucippe

- - - ◆ - - -

WINGSPAN: *c.80mm (3in)*
RANGE: *Asia*

Anyone who fancies seeing this mouthwateringly citrus-coloured butterfly needs to prepare for an expedition. Of all the species featured in this book, *Hebomoia leucippe* lives in the most remote place – small islands in a particularly out-of-the-way region of the Indonesia archipelago. I use its scientific name advisedly, for this butterfly is so obscure that it has no unequivocal English moniker. I have plumped for brimstone wing, but other alternatives include fire orange-tip and vibrant sulphur.

With its vibrantly orange wingtips, the brimstone wing may look vaguely familiar. Indeed, it is a member of the whites family (Pieridae), whose representatives in this book include the superficially similar-looking orange-

tip (*Anthocharis cardamines*) and the notorious large white (*Pieris brassicae*). But that's where any affinities cease.

The brimstone wing inhabits five islands in Maluku (Moluccas) province and one in the Banggai group, off the southeast coast of Sulawesi. Put those six landforms together, and the total area from which this butterfly is known only marginally exceeds the size of Belgium. Such a restricted range risks putting the brimstone wing at potential threat of extinction. Furthermore, it inhabits tropical rainforest – and one-quarter of Indonesia's already depleted forest was razed to the ground in the 15 years to 2005.

Although unlikely in the medium term at least, the brimstone wing's demise would not only be a tragedy in its own right – extinction is for ever – but as a symbol of our wider disdain for both the history of discovery and the future of our planet. Maluku and Sulawesi form part of the biogeographical realm known as Wallacea, a region separated by deep-water straits from both continental Asia and Australasia. Its name honours Alfred Russel Wallace, whose explorations here and subsequent cogitations were critical to his formulation – independently of Charles Darwin – of the theory of evolution through natural selection.